{contents}

Words that are printed in bold, **like this**, are explained in the Glossary on page 46.

{our world}

Imagine you get home hungry after school and the fridge is empty. Time to go to the shops and buy more food. That's a simple solution to a simple problem. If you run out of **resources**, the things you need, you get some more. Unfortunately, some of the world's resources are less easy to replace.

Different resources

People take lots of natural resources from the world around them, such as freshwater to drink or oil to power machines. The trouble is that some of these resources are in very short supply. Once they are all used up there will be no more. These are **non-renewable resources**.

Other natural resources such as trees are **renewable**. This means they can be replaced and should not run out. The trouble is that in some places people are using up trees too fast. They don't give them time to regrow.

What the world needs to do in the future is use resources in a **sustainable** way. That means use them carefully so they do not run out.

These fishermen do not fish in the same place all the time. They move on so that they do not use up all the fish resources in one place.

10/07

DATE DUE FOR RETURN

Renewals
www.liverpool.gov.uk/libraries
0151 233 3000

{geography focus}

A SUSTAINABLE FUTURE

{saving & recycling resources}

Louise Spilsbury

www.raintreepublishers.co.uk

Visit our website to find out more information about **Raintree** books.

To order:

 Phone 44 (0) 1865 888112

 Send a fax to 44 (0) 1865 314091

 Visit the Raintree Bookshop at **www.raintreepublishers.co.uk** to browse our catalogue and order online.

First published 2006 by Heinemann Library a division of Harcourt Education Australia, 20 Thackray Road, Port Melbourne Victoria 3207 Australia (a division of Reed International Books Australia Pty Ltd, ABN 70 001 002 357). Visit the Heinemann Library website at www.heinemannlibrary.com.au

Published in Great Britain in 2006 by Raintree, Halley Court, Jordan Hill, Oxford OX2 8EJ, part of Harcourt Education www.raintreepublishers.co.uk

 A Reed Elsevier company

© Reed International Books Australia Pty Ltd 2006

13 digit ISBN 978 1 740 70274 4
10 09 08 07
10 9 8 7 6 5 4 3 2

Editorial: Moira Anderson, Carmel Heron, Diyan Leake, Patrick Catel
Cover, text design & graphs: Marta White
Photo research: Karen Forsythe, Wendy Duncan
Production: Tracey Jarrett, Duncan Gilbert
Map diagrams: Guy Holt
Technical diagrams: Nives Porcellato & Andy Craig

Typeset in 12/17.5 pt Gill Sans Regular
Origination by Modern Age
Printed and bound in China Leo Paper Group
Printing Company Ltd

National Library of Australia Cataloguing-in-Publication data:

Spilsbury, Louise.
    A sustainable future : saving and recycling resources.

    Includes index.
    For upper primary and lower secondary school students.
    ISBN 1 74070 274 3.

    1. Sustainable development – Juvenile literature.
    2. Energy conservation – Juvenile literature.
    3. Recycling (Waste, etc.) – Juvenile literature. I. Title.
    (Series: Spilsbury, Louise. Geography focus).

338.927

Acknowledgements

The publisher would like to thank the following for permission to reproduce copyright material: APL/Corbis/Pallava Bagla: p. **30**, /Collart Herve: p. **24**, /Gideon Mendel: p. **6**, /Warren Morgan: p. **18**, /Howell Paul: p. **21** (lower), /Ricki Rosen: p. **34**, /David Sailors: p. **26**, /George Shelley: p. **28**, /Anthony John West: p. **16**; Imagen/Bill Thomas: pp. **8**, **33**; Lonely Planet Images/Manfred Gottschalk: p. **4**, /Jonathan Smith: p. **10**, /Eric Wheater: p. **43**; NASA: p. **21** (upper); Photolibrary.com/ Photo Researchers: p. **14**, /Science Photo Library/Robert Brook: p. **22**, /Science Photo Library/Adam Hart-Davis: p. **38**; StockXchange: p. **40**; Reuters/Picture Media/Yun Suk-Bong: p. **32**; University of Illinois, College of ACES: p. **41**. All other images PhotoDisc.

Cover photograph of mountain meadow and inset image of wind farm reproduced with permission of PhotoDisc.

Every attempt has been made to trace and acknowledge copyright. Where an attempt has been unsuccessful, the publisher would be pleased to hear from the copyright owner so any omission or error can be rectified.

Wasting and spoiling resources

Most people use up more resources than they need. You waste water if you leave the tap on when brushing your teeth. You waste electricity if you leave lights on after you've left a room.

People also spoil or **pollute** resources. For example, people drop litter in rivers. We all throw away things we have bought and this creates rubbish. When we waste or pollute resources, other people and other living things cannot use them.

Footprints

Some people in the world use more resources and make more waste than others. An **environmental footprint** is a way of comparing how sustainable we are. It is the area of land that could provide all the resources a person needs, and deal with the waste they produce. The smaller the footprint, the more sustainable the person is and the better it is for our planet.

You can see on the map that the average person from the USA has a much larger footprint than the average person from Africa. This is because most people in the USA use more resources, such as oil and water, and produce more pollution than most Africans.

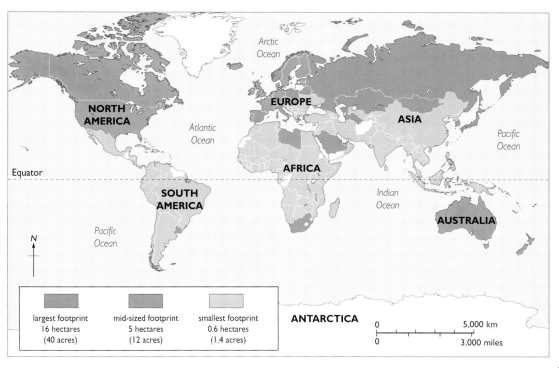

A world map showing environmental footprint. (No information was available for white areas.)

{waste not, want not!}

The number of people on Earth is growing. Increasing numbers of people means increased pressure on the planet. At present rates of **resource** use we are already spoiling many parts of Earth. Parts of the world's oceans are being emptied of fish. Large areas of rainforest are being chopped down.

We can help to use fewer resources by cutting down on waste. We can use only the resources that we need to sustain us and leave enough for people in the future. This is **sustainable** living. If we want to live sustainably, we need to reduce the size of our **environmental footprint**.

The three Rs

The three rules of reducing waste are the three Rs. The first R is for reduce. This means reduce the resources we use. For example, take your own reusable bags to carry away your supermarket shopping. Try to use less of the new plastic bags the shop gives out.

People can come up with lots of ingenious ways of using stuff rather than throwing it away. These toys are made from old tins.

The second R is for reuse. This means reuse things rather than throw them away. For example, mend your old bike and give or sell it to someone else to ride.

The third R is for recycle. **Recycling** is when things we throw away are converted into something else. For example, used plastic bottles can be turned into a fleece jacket.

This book will look at how people can use the three Rs to help our planet by using fewer resources, wasting less, and creating less rubbish.

FACT!

Each year people use one trillion (that's one million million) plastic bags!

Recycling league

Some countries recycle more of their rubbish than others. This bar chart shows how much rubbish different countries recycle. The recycling values are percentages, which means the share of the total rubbish produced. Not all these countries produce the same amount of rubbish. You can see that Austria recycles 64 percent of its rubbish, which is eight times as much as Greece does.

Charts like this don't tell the whole story. For example, Greece produces less rubbish than Austria to start with. But they do show us that many countries could be recycling more.

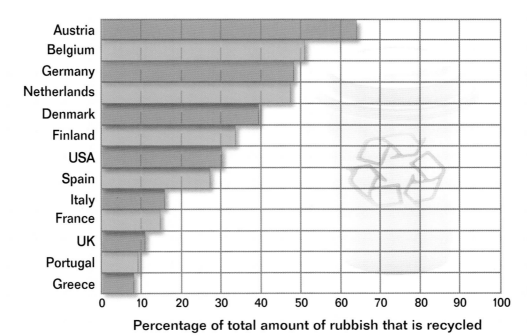

Percentage of total amount of rubbish that is recycled

A bar chart comparing recycling rates in different countries.

{energy}

People around the world need energy to power their lives. We use electrical energy to make machines such as computers work. We use heat energy to cook our food and to warm the buildings we live, work, and study in.

Three-quarters of all of this energy comes from **fossil fuels**. Fossil fuels are natural **resources** including oil, gas, and coal that we burn to make energy. More than half the world's electricity is made in **power stations**. These special factories burn coal or gas to boil water and make steam. The steam turns giant wheels called **turbines** that spin magnets to create electricity.

Fossil fuel problems

Fossil fuels are a **non-renewable resource** and they cause **pollution**. When we burn fossil fuels we release polluting gases such as sulphur dioxide and carbon dioxide into the air. Sulphur dioxide can mix with rain to make **acid rain** and also cause health problems in people.

Take a look around your home and count the number of electrical machines that are switched on every evening.

Carbon dioxide is essential for plants to live. It also is essential in creating the Earth's **greenhouse effect**, which traps the Sun's heat next to the Earth, warming it to temperatures that can sustain life. Increasing amounts of carbon dioxide, however, are causing an increased greenhouse effect that is gradually raising temperatures and affecting weather around the planet. This is affecting the survival of different animals and plants. **Global warming** threatens to melt **ice caps** on Earth. The extra water in the oceans will cause rising sea levels that could affect coastal towns and villages.

FACT!

If we carry on using fossil fuels at the same rate as we do today, the world's oil will run out by 2030, gas by 2040 and coal by 2200.

What are fossil fuels?

Fossil fuels are made from fossils, the preserved remains of living things that died millions of years ago. This diagram shows how coal formed. After prehistoric trees died, they were buried in mud. The remains squashed together and slowly rotted into **peat**. This peat gradually turned into hard coal. The mud turned to rock, trapping the fossil fuels. Oil and gas formed in a similar way from tiny animals that lived in ancient seas.

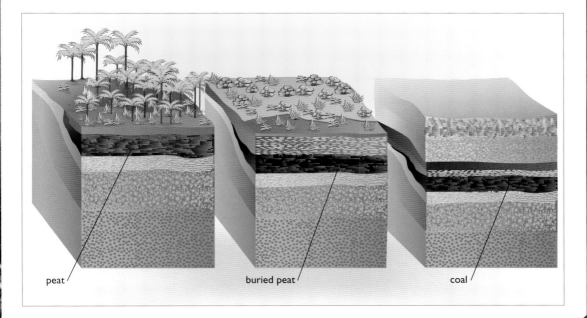

peat   buried peat   coal

Diagram explaining how coal forms.

{using less energy}

It is possible to reduce the amount of fuel energy we use. This saves money on fuel bills. It means **fossil fuels** will not run out so fast. It also means there is less **pollution** from burning fuel.

Heating buildings

In colder places, many buildings are centrally heated with boilers. Boilers burn fossil fuels to heat water. The hot water moves through pipes to metal radiators in different rooms. The hot water warms the metal, heating the air around the radiator. We can keep the air warm by **insulating** our buildings. The simplest ways to trap the warm air inside are to make sure doors are closed and windows are double-glazed. We will then use less fuel to keep our buildings warm.

FACT!

Turning down the central heating by just 1°C (1.8°F) cuts the average boiler fuel bill by 10 percent.

After it snows, a completely clear roof on a house may mean that warm air has risen from inside and melted the snow.

Electricity

We can all reduce the amount of electricity we use. The simplest way is to switch off lights and electrical machines completely when they are not in use. A TV or computer on standby uses up half the power of one switched on. Another way is to use our machines more efficiently. Washing machines use as much electricity to wash a half load as a full load of dirty clothes. So always wash full loads.

We can also buy machines with high-energy ratings, such as some new dishwashers and fridges. This means they use less electricity to run. Low-energy light bulbs have better energy ratings and last longer than normal bulbs.

A world divided

We can divide the countries of the world into two types. Richer, **more-developed countries** are mostly in the northern half of the world. Poorer, **less-developed countries** are mostly in the south. More-developed countries use more fossil fuels for energy and create more pollution than less-developed countries.

The chart shows how much polluting carbon dioxide an average person produces from six different countries. You can see that the average person in the more-developed USA produces 20 tonnes (22 tons) of carbon dioxide per year. But each person from less-developed China produces 2 tonnes (2.2 tons), one-tenth of this amount.

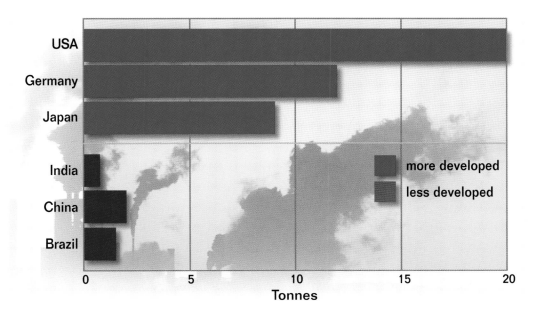

This bar chart shows the tonnes of carbon dioxide produced per person each year in different countries.

{renewable energy sources}

About one-quarter of the energy people use around the world is **renewable**. That means it comes from sources such as the Sun, moving wind, and water. These sources are **sustainable** and will not run out like **fossil fuels**.

Water and wind power

In many mountainous areas on Earth, such as parts of the USA and Nepal, people rely on moving water to make electricity. River and reservoir water is directed downhill through pipes. The fast moving water spins **turbines** at the bottom. These turn generators, creating electricity called hydropower or water power. The water is pumped to the top again to make more hydropower.

People also use seawater to make power. They use special machines to convert the up-and-down movement of waves or tides into electricity.

Wind power can only be used in windy places, often near coasts or on hills. Tall turbines twist to face the blowing wind so they can spin faster and make more electricity.

Wind farms are large groups of wind turbines that together make lots of electricity.

Light and heat power

Other renewable energy sources are light and heat from the Sun and heat from inside the Earth. People can turn sunlight into electricity using **solar cells** (see case study on page 15). They also use solar collectors on their roofs to heat water to wash with or to use in central heating. Solar collectors use heat from the Sun to warm up water in thin pipes.

Our other main source of natural heat is from hot rock deep underground. In areas where the rock is nearest the surface, people can use **geothermal** energy.

Renewable energy and the environment

Making renewable energy creates very little **pollution**. It also uses no **non-renewable resources**. That's why most people believe it is good for the environment. However, not everyone agrees completely. For example, some people think wind farms spoil the countryside, are noisy, and harm flying birds. They argue it would take too many wind farms to make enough electricity to replace power stations.

Types of renewable energy

How important are the different types of renewable energy? This pie chart shows which sorts give us the most power today. You can see the most important renewable energy source is **biomass**. This is fuel made from animal or plant waste that would otherwise rot away. (See page 40 for more information.) The other important renewable energy source is hydropower. But in the future, solar and geothermal power could provide much more of our energy.

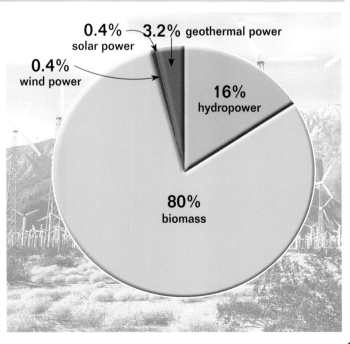

0.4% solar power — 3.2% geothermal power
0.4% wind power
16% hydropower
80% biomass

This pie chart shows world renewable energy consumption.

{case study} solar-powered school

Medina High School in southern England, UK, had a leaking roof. The staff and students decided they wanted to replace it with a special roof containing **solar cells**. They wanted to save money by making their own electricity. They also wanted to help reduce air **pollution**. Solar cells make no polluting gases as they work.

Overcoming problems

The trouble is that solar cells are expensive. Medina High needed a lot of solar cells to make enough electricity. The staff and governors found some help. They got the government to help them pay for their solar roof.

The roof is made of panels of solar cells. These were built into thick sheets of waterproof, flexible plastic. The plastic sheets were attached to the flat wooden roof of the school. The solar panels were then wired into the school's electricity system.

This roof is made of panels of solar cells.

14

Solar benefits

The solar roof now makes enough electricity to power all the school's 46 computers and other electrical equipment. During school holidays any spare power is sold back to the school's electricity supplier. This money helps to pay for any power that the school has to buy at busier times of the year.

Students can check how the roof is performing using special software on the school's computers. By knowing more about the benefits of solar power they can all learn more about **sustainable** living, too.

Solar cells

A solar cell is made of two thin layers of silicon sandwiched between clear glass or plastic. Silicon is a material that can be made from sand or found in big lumps in some rocks. The two layers of the cell are slightly different sorts of silicon. When sunlight shines on the upper layer, it makes a tiny electric current move to the lower layer. The cell makes more power when it is sunnier. Panels of solar cells produce a much larger current than a single cell. The more cells and panels people fit, the more electricity they can make.

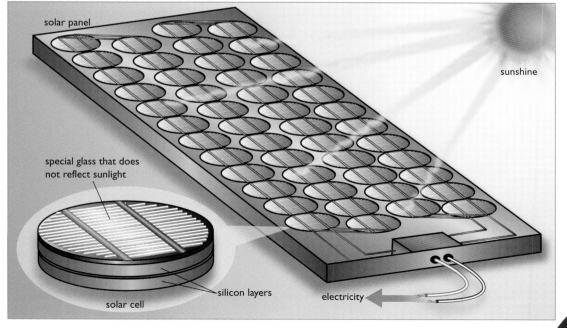

solar panel

sunshine

special glass that does
not reflect sunlight

silicon layers

solar cell

electricity

This diagram shows how solar panels work.

{transport troubles}

Today many people can travel more cheaply, more widely, and faster than ever before. There are great benefits to modern transport. People fly around the world for holidays, drive, or take a bus or train to work, school, or college every day. However, there are problems too.

Invisible dangers

Nearly all vehicle engines burn **fossil fuels** and release **polluting** exhaust smoke into the air. Particles and poisonous gases in the smoke cause many people to have breathing problems. They can even cause serious illnesses such as **cancer**. Carbon dioxide in the smoke contributes towards **global warming**. When smoke mixes with water droplets in clouds it forms **acid rain**, which can kill trees and fish. In the UK alone, transport pollution increased by half between 1990 and 2002.

FACT!

Aeroplanes are responsible for a huge amount of pollution:

- One-tenth of carbon dioxide pollution in the atmosphere comes from aeroplanes.

- By 2015 there will be double the air travel of 1995.

- One in eight people in the UK is affected by aircraft noise pollution.

There are so many aeroplanes in use that the sky can sometimes be filled with the white lines of cloud they leave behind.

Big car trouble

Today there are more than 600 million cars on Earth! Many new cars are small with good fuel economy. This means they travel a long distance for each bit of fuel. But some new 4x4 cars are very big, polluting, and have bad fuel economy. They use a litre of petrol to travel less than 3 kilometres (2 miles). Their heavy engines are high off the ground, sometimes at chest level. Some experts believe a person is 30 times more likely to be killed by a 4 x 4 in a car accident than by a normal car.

Fuel economy

This graph shows how fuel economy changed in the USA from 1975 to 2000. Back in the 1970s petrol was very cheap in the USA. Small vehicles, including cars and small trucks, had low fuel economy, travelling 5 kilometres (3 miles) per litre (kpL). Between 1985 and 1990, petrol cost more. So vehicles were built with more efficient engines that could manage 9 kpL. Since then, fuel economy has dropped as fuel has got cheaper again and cars such as 4 x 4s are using more.

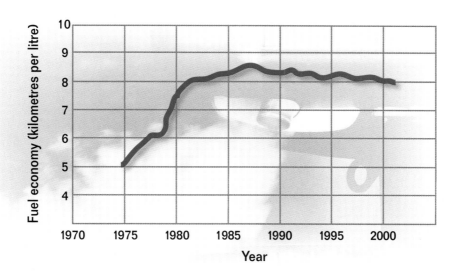

This graph shows changing fuel economy in the USA, from 1975 to 2000.

17

{getting there}

Sustainable transport moves people efficiently and produces the minimum amount of **pollution**. There are many ways to make transport more sustainable.

Use cars less

People can leave the car at home and allow time to walk or cycle to school or work. It is sustainable and healthy. Networks of safe cycle paths are common in countries such as the Netherlands and parts of the UK. If a trip is too far to walk or cycle, people can reduce pollution by sharing cars instead of travelling separately.

Some governments try to put people off using their cars, especially in towns and cities where they could use cheap public transport. For example, they make people pay to drive on busy roads.

FACT!

- In the UK, between 8 and 9 a.m., one in five cars on the roads is carrying children to school. This is the school run.

- Each year the UK school run uses enough fuel to fill 1000 petrol tankers.

- Most journeys are less than 3 kilometres (2 miles). Short car trips are more polluting per kilometre than long ones.

Cycling is a fun, healthy activity, and a sustainable way of getting around.

Making less pollution

Many people have to use cars to get around. They can help cut down pollution. For example, they can buy a vehicle with better fuel economy or switch off their engine when stationary. More and more vehicles are fitted with catalytic converters, devices that clean up their exhaust smoke.

People can also use cleaner fuel in vehicles. In US states such as Iowa, petrol is mixed with alcohol made from maize (corn) **crop** waste. When alcohol burns it produces steam, so this mix makes less pollution than petrol alone. Battery-powered cars and buses do not even use fuel. They just need to be recharged when they have run out of power.

How polluting is your transport?

This bar chart compares how much carbon dioxide different forms of transport make. Walking and cycling are clearly the winners in **sustainable** transport. You can see that buses are the most polluting, but as they can carry lots of people, each person on a bus is less polluting than one in a car. So, one person in a small car causes two and a half times more pollution than if he or she goes by bus.

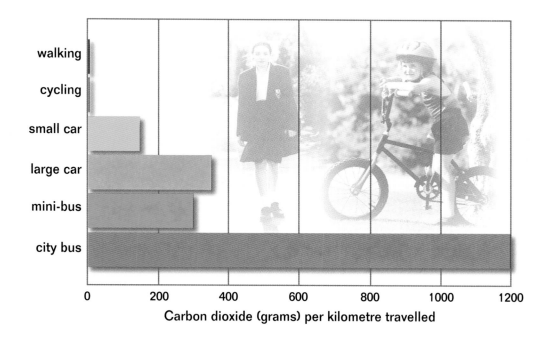

Carbon dioxide (grams) per kilometre travelled

This bar chart shows how much carbon dioxide various methods of getting to school make.

{wasting water}

There is the same amount of water on Earth today as there was millions of years ago. The problem is that water supplies that people, livestock, and wildlife can use are not spread evenly around the Earth. Some places simply do not have as much water as they need. In places where people should have enough, there may be shortages because people waste too much. And in others the water is so **polluted** it is harmful to use and goes to waste.

Who wastes or pollutes water?

Farmers use up nearly three-quarters of all freshwater to **irrigate** their **crops** and let their livestock drink. Lots of irrigation water is wasted before plants can suck it up and use it to grow. Some soaks into the ground and some **evaporates** into the air.

Water in rivers, lakes, and oceans is polluted by waste from factories and farms. The waste includes livestock manure and chemicals used to make goods such as leather.

Water on Earth

Almost all water on our planet is seawater that is too salty for most land plants and animals to use. Three-quarters of all freshwater is trapped as solid ice around the North and South Poles. Of the rest, some makes up the bodies of living things and some is **water vapour** in the air. The remainder is found as **groundwater**, in rivers, streams, reservoirs, and lakes. This is the water we can use.

Earth is called the blue planet because it is mainly covered in salty 'blue' seawater.

The lost sea

Just 50 years ago, the Aral Sea in Central Asia (see photo, right) was a healthy sea with an area of 66,000 square kilometres (25,500 square miles). This is a little smaller than the Irish Republic. The Aral Sea had a large fishing fleet and thriving towns around its edges. Today it is less than two-thirds its original size. It is too salty for many fish to live in. Once-busy ports are now stranded far from its shores like ghost towns (see photo below).

The reason the sea shrank is that farmers took too much water out of the rivers that feed into the sea. They took water to irrigate cotton and rice crops. The land around the sea is turning to desert and is too dry for crops.

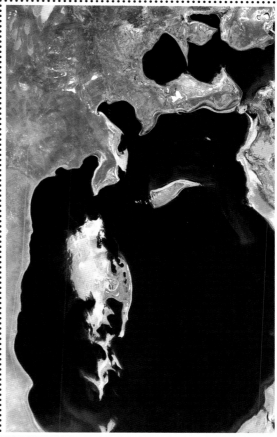

The Aral Sea 50 years ago (top) and one of its deserted ports today (above).

{saving water}

Water is the most precious **resource** on Earth. Without it most living things die. How can people ensure they use it **sustainably**?

Industry

In many **more-developed countries**, industry is already using less water. Water is reused several times or recycled rather than using fresh water each time. For example, since 1990 the Swedish paper industry has doubled the amount of paper it makes but halved the amount of water it uses. In **less-developed countries** more water is wasted and **pollution** is less carefully controlled than in more-developed countries. In less-developed China, it takes around 40,000 litres (9,000 gallons) of water to make a tonne of steel. In more-developed Japan it takes just 8,000 litres (1,800 gallons). New machinery and technology is needed to improve water saving in such industries.

*Farmers can reduce water pollution in several ways. **Organic** farmers use no chemicals on their **crops**. This farmer, who uses chemicals, has created a buffer zone between his field and a river. This is a band of land to stop chemicals washing into the river.*

Home and garden

There are so many ways to save water in your home. Every time you shower instead of having a bath, you can save up to 45 litres (10 gallons) of water. Don't fill the kettle full to make a hot drink. Only boil enough water for what you need.

Try not to use tapwater in the garden to water plants. Instead, collect rainwater from a barrel connected to your roof gutters. You could also reuse bath water for the garden. Bury cut-off bottle tops or tubes in soil next to the roots of trees then water close to the roots. The bottle tops or tubes are effective at collecting water.

Flushed with success

On average each person goes to the toilet five to ten times a day. They use about 12 litres (2.6 gallons) to flush each time. This pie chart shows the average proportions of water used each day for different purposes by a Canadian person. You can see they use one-third of the water flushing.

People can easily make their toilet flush less water. They do this by reducing the space inside the **cistern** using a brick or a special plastic bag. Then they only flush 8 litres (1.8 gallons).

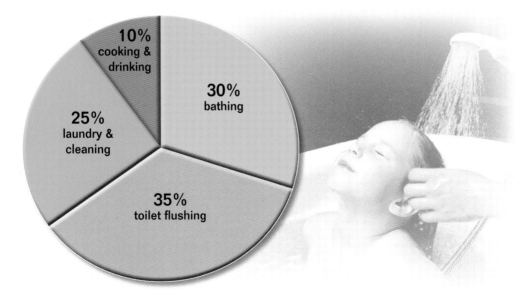

This pie chart shows how much of the total water usage an average Canadian takes for different purposes.

{tree tales}

Trees are an incredibly useful **resource**. We can use their wood to make lots of things, from buildings and furniture to pencils and paper. But this is nothing compared to their greatest importance. Trees are vital to the health of our planet.

Cleaning up and soaking up

Trees are green plants. They use **photosynthesis** to make their own food in their leaves. One ingredient for photosynthesis is carbon dioxide from the air. Just one tree can remove 30 kilograms (66 pounds) of **pollution** from the air. As they make food, trees produce oxygen. Without the oxygen green plants make, people would not be able to breathe.

Forests and the soil their roots hold together also soak up rain. The water then slowly filters into the ground to top up **groundwater**. Without forests, rain runs fast off land into rivers, sometimes causing flooding.

*Brazil is the country with the most tropical forest and also the country with the highest **deforestation** rate.*

Disappearing forests

Trees can be a **renewable** resource if used carefully. The trouble is that people are chopping down forests much too fast. They are doing this, for example, to clear land to grow **crops** or to get timber to make matches or plywood. Deforestation is a major global problem.

FACT!

Half a hectare (1.24 acres) of rainforest is lost every second.

Deforestation

Since people have been living on Earth they have chopped down half of all its forests. On this map the light-coloured areas show the forest area of 8,000 years ago. The darker areas show present forests. In **temperate** areas such as Europe, forest has been gradually destroyed over thousands of years as people have cleared land for farming and building. The present rate of deforestation is very low.

In **tropical** areas the situation is very different. Deforestation started around 500 years ago when Europeans started to live in tropical places. The deforestation rate has been increasing since then. The worst rate was between 1980 and 1995. A total area of tropical forest the size of the whole country of Indonesia was chopped down. Apart from farming, a big danger for tropical forests today is **logging** for valuable timber.

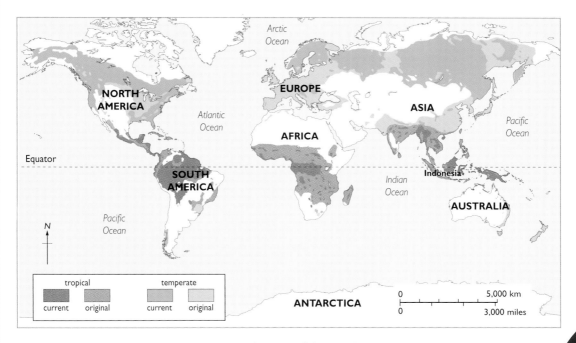

This map shows original and remaining forests of the world.

{saving trees}

How can we help to save the Earth's forests? One answer is to avoid buying wood from endangered natural forests. Instead buy new timber, furniture, paper, or other products made from trees grown in **sustainable** forests or **plantations**. In these forests quick-growing trees such as pine or eucalypts are grown to replace those cut down. Plantations covering just 3 percent of forest land on Earth could provide all the wood we need to make paper and building materials.

Reduce, recycle, and reuse

We can also save trees using the three Rs. We first have to ask ourselves whether we could reduce the new wood products we buy. For example, could I read a book out of the library or buy secondhand rather than buying a new one? When we've finished with something made from wood, such as a newspaper, could we **recycle** it?

These huge piles of magazines and newspapers are waiting to be recycled.

26

We can reuse all sorts of products made from trees rather than buying new ones. Buying secondhand furniture or timber is sustainable and cheaper. Instead of reaching for a new sheet of paper, write or draw on the other side. Why not save your Christmas wrapping paper to use again next year? Old cardboard boxes and packaging can be reused as containers or something more imaginative if you are creative enough.

FACT!

People can choose to buy timber or furniture with a green Forest Stewardship Council or FSC stamp on it. Then they know it comes from sustainable forests.

Trees and recycling

In the UK, one-quarter of all the waste people throw away is paper, made from trees. If everyone in the USA recycled just one out of every ten newspapers or magazines bought, they would save 25 million trees a year. Sixty percent of newspaper is made from recycled paper. Newspaper is also used for pet bedding, cat litter, and roof insulation.

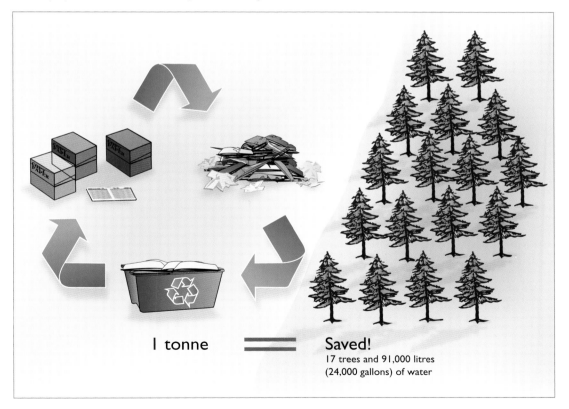

1 tonne === Saved!
17 trees and 91,000 litres (24,000 gallons) of water

This diagram shows how we can save trees and water by recycling 1 tonne (1.1 ton) of paper.

{the stuff we buy}

We live in a global market. This means many people have access to products from around the world, not just local stuff. They can buy from shops but also online, at any time of day or night. They have so much choice they can easily shop around for the cheapest prices.

We really need some stuff, such as some food or medicines. But we buy other stuff just because we want it. Many new things are made to replace what we already have. For example, we buy more powerful games consoles, mp3 players that can play more tracks than a personal CD player, and new fashions such as trainers.

Shopping and resources

Making new stuff wastes lots of the world's **resources**. For example, to make one new computer chip it takes a total of 1.6 kilograms (3.5 pounds) of **fossil fuel**, 72 grams (2.5 ounces) of chemicals and 32 kilograms (70 pounds) of water. The fossil fuel alone is 800 times the weight of the tiny, 2-gram chip. It takes a lot of resources to make chips because they are small and difficult to handle. They also have to be made in special dirt-free conditions.

*Shop till you drop! Shopping for luxuries is big business all over the **more-developed** world.*

Shopping makes waste

Buying stuff also creates waste. Few new things are made to last because they will eventually be replaced with newer stuff. Many new things are difficult to take apart, making **recycling** of their components difficult. There are enough dumped, out-of-date computers in the USA to fill 6,000 Olympic swimming pools!

Made in Indonesia, and Korea, and the USA ...

What is the real cost of a pair of trainers, not just in money, but in how their manufacture affects people and the planet's resources?

The leather for a pair of trainers comes from cattle in Texas, USA (A). It is sent to South Korean factories (B) to be processed. The strong chemicals they use have polluted parts of Korean rivers so much that the water is undrinkable. The rubber for the soles is made partly from oil from Saudi Arabia (C). The person who sews and sticks the trainers together in Indonesia (D) gets £1 a day. She may get sick from the glue fumes she breathes in. A pair of these trainers costs £75 in UK shops (E).

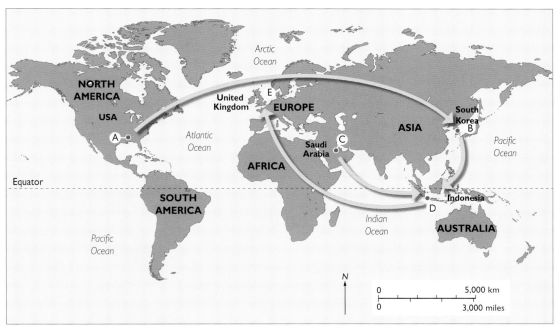

This world map shows where components for some trainers come from and where they are assembled.

{case study}
the tale of a T-shirt

Have you ever thought how your favourite T-shirt was made? The tale of a
T-shirt starts with cotton plants. These grow in warm parts of the world,
in places such as China, India, and the southern USA.

From plant to shirt

Cotton plants grow for half a year before
they are ready to harvest. They are then
covered in brown seed pods called bolls
which split open revealing white fluff inside.
The fluff, or cotton wool, is made of fibres,
up to 4 centimetres (2 inches) long, that
surround cotton seeds. It is these fibres
farmers sell to make cotton.

Picking the fluffy, white cotton bolls.

To make a T-shirt

This is a flow diagram to show the steps in making a T-shirt and the **resources**
used. The yellow steps would not be used if the cotton were grown organically.

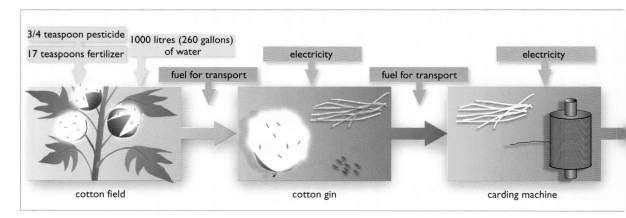

3/4 teaspoon pesticide

17 teaspoons fertilizer

1000 litres (260 gallons) of water

fuel for transport

electricity

fuel for transport

electricity

cotton field

cotton gin

carding machine

The production process of making a cotton T-shirt from plant to shop.

The bolls are picked and fed into cotton gins, which are machines that separate fibres from seeds. This thread is woven into fabric for a T-shirt.

Chemical cotton

Most cotton farmers use chemicals to help them grow as much cotton as possible. They spray **fertilizers** on their fields to make the plants grow bigger. They spray **pesticides** to kill the insects that like to eat cotton bolls.

Pesticides can harm people. Pesticides poison around three million farm workers in **less-developed countries** every year. Pesticides kill wildlife and living things in soil that help keep it healthy. They **pollute** rivers, **groundwater**, and the air.

Pesticides stick to the cotton fibres. Then other **polluting** chemicals are used to bleach the fibres, dye the cloth and to stop the finished T-shirt getting creased.

Organic cotton

Some farmers grow cotton for T-shirts without using chemicals. They prevent pests from eating bolls by removing them by hand. They encourage pest-eating insects and birds to live on their farms. More bolls are damaged than in chemical farming, so **organic** cotton sells for a higher price.

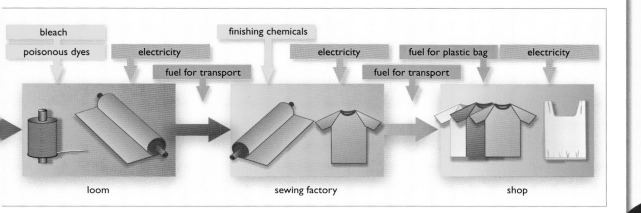

{ buy better and buy less }

We make lots of choices when we shop. We might choose only to buy our T-shirt because we like the brand or simply buy the cheapest. We should be trying to buy the best for the planet.

Sustainable choices

People can make a difference by choosing to buy more **sustainable** goods. These are goods that have been made using fewer **resources**, have produced less waste, and have **polluted** less. They might also be **fair trade** goods (see box right). When you buy fair trade you pay a fair price to the producer.

What does fair trade mean for farmers and producers?

- They are paid a fair price for their goods that doesn't change from month to month.

- Their goods are bought year after year. With regular money coming in, they can plan for the future and make life better for their communities, for example by building schools or health centres.

- They are advised on how to use fewer polluting chemicals and to have safer and fairer working conditions.

The global Buy Nothing Day campaign reminds people that they have a choice about whether they buy or not.

Made to last

We can also choose to buy things that last. For example, an **organic** T-shirt might last for longer, be comfier and wash better each time than one made of cotton grown chemically. You usually pay more for things designed to last, because the raw materials cost more. But over time, these goods need replacing less. For example, an energy-saving washing machine made in a sustainable factory costs more but lasts for twenty years. If you buy a cheaper machine that only lasts five years, you would need to replace it four times in the twenty years. It is cheaper over twenty years to buy the better machine.

Wearing more for less

Secondhand clothes shops are great places to find stylish, quality garments that cost much less than in new clothes chops. If your style changes, you can always swap what you don't want for something different. By reusing perfectly good clothes you can help prevent waste and have fun dressing up.

Buying secondhand clothes helps the planet's resources and can help you dress better for less money.

{household waste}

What do you throw in the bin? Maybe apple cores, empty drink cans, odd socks, plastic bags, or a drawing you messed up. Once a week people take all this household waste away. What happens to it then?

Dumped or burnt

Lots of waste is dumped in enormous holes in the ground called **landfill sites** to rot. Lots of waste is burnt in special furnaces called **incinerators**. Some waste is **recycled**. When a landfill site is full, it is covered over with soil and a new site is dug. As waste rots and squashes, it releases gases and a liquid called **leachate**. These can **pollute** air, land, and water. Rotting waste smells and also attracts pests such as rats.

The biggest problem with incinerators is the polluting smoke that they release into the air. Japan burns nearly three-quarters of its waste. People who live near incinerators are more likely to develop **cancers** because they breathe in poisonous dioxin gas from the smoke.

Vast amounts of waste are dumped in landfill sites all over the world.

Most incinerators use a lot of **fossil fuels** to burn the waste. However, some run on gas from rotting rubbish and even generate electricity. They get rid of waste much quicker than landfill sites so it does not pile up on land. But this can make people put less effort into recycling and reducing how much waste they make.

Biodegradable waste

Natural waste on the ground such as dead animals, fallen leaves, or fruit rots away naturally. It is **biodegradable**. This means **decomposers** such as **bacteria** break it down. Over half our waste, such as paper and vegetable peelings, is biodegradable and rots away within months. Around one-third of waste, such as plastic bags, nappies, cans, or glass jars, is non-biodegradable waste. It takes tens to thousands of years to break down, without decomposers.

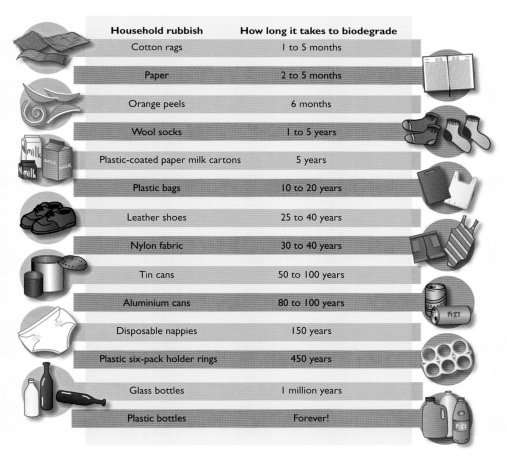

Household rubbish	How long it takes to biodegrade
Cotton rags	1 to 5 months
Paper	2 to 5 months
Orange peels	6 months
Wool socks	1 to 5 years
Plastic-coated paper milk cartons	5 years
Plastic bags	10 to 20 years
Leather shoes	25 to 40 years
Nylon fabric	30 to 40 years
Tin cans	50 to 100 years
Aluminium cans	80 to 100 years
Disposable nappies	150 years
Plastic six-pack holder rings	450 years
Glass bottles	1 million years
Plastic bottles	Forever!

This chart compares how long it takes some common items of rubbish to biodegrade.

{recycling}

Glass bottles, newspapers, plastic bottles, metal cans … It is possible to **recycle** over three-quarters of all our household waste. More recycling means less waste put in **landfill sites** and burnt in **incinerators**. Recycling is also a **sustainable** way of using **resources**. For example, recycling the glass in a bottle uses far fewer resources and much less energy than making new glass from raw materials.

But most people do not recycle enough. In the UK, for example, people recycle only 11 percent of their waste. The rest goes in the bin.

Getting sorted

It is easiest to recycle waste when householders sort it out. In **more-developed countries** people are given different-coloured plastic bags and bins to put different types of waste into. In other places they have bottle banks, paper banks, and can banks on their streets.

Capital plan

The capital city of Australia, Canberra, wants to close its two landfill sites by the year 2010. Canberra's government is encouraging its 300,000 people to recycle nearly all their waste. It is probably the largest city on the planet with a 'no waste' plan.

Many countries have recycling bins like this one, to collect cans, bottles, and used paper to be recycled.

It is possible for waste workers to sort out mixed waste from bins. They put waste on conveyor belts to pick out plastic by hand and steel using magnets. But this process takes time and costs money. Also, the sorted waste will be covered in rotting food and whatever else was in the bin with it.

The next step

Once waste is sorted into different types, it is transported to special factories that can recycle particular materials. For example, aluminium cans are squashed together in large blocks and taken to aluminium recycling plants.

Resources in waste

Recycling is all about thinking of waste as a resource that is useful to make other things. This pie chart shows the proportions of different types of waste people in the UK throw in their bins. Around the edge of the chart are some of the products that can be made from this waste if it is recycled.

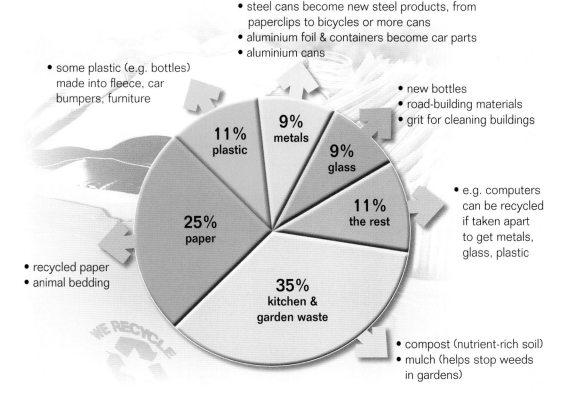

- steel cans become new steel products, from paperclips to bicycles or more cans
- aluminium foil & containers become car parts
- aluminium cans

- some plastic (e.g. bottles) made into fleece, car bumpers, furniture

- new bottles
- road-building materials
- grit for cleaning buildings

- e.g. computers can be recycled if taken apart to get metals, glass, plastic

- recycled paper
- animal bedding

- compost (nutrient-rich soil)
- mulch (helps stop weeds in gardens)

11% plastic

9% metals

9% glass

11% the rest

25% paper

35% kitchen & garden waste

This pie chart shows what goes into bins (in the UK) and what the waste could be recycled into.

{case study} from can to can!

It takes about two months to convert a waste aluminium drinks can into a **recycled** new one.

Reclaiming metal

The process starts with blocks of crushed cans arriving at an aluminium recycling plant. Here workers tip the blocks into a hot furnace. The temperature inside is about 700 °C (1,300 °F). That's three times hotter than a pizza oven. The heat melts the cans into a liquid, which is poured into moulds. The chunks of aluminium that form in the moulds as the liquid cools are called ingots.

Making cans

These ingots are transported from the recycling plant to factories that make cans. The recycled ingots are fed into machines that roll the metal into vast, thin sheets. Other machines stamp out sides and bottoms for cans from the aluminium sheets. They print colours and labels on the pieces.

FACT!

Enough aluminium cans were recycled between 1972 and 2005 to stretch end-to-end from Earth to the Moon and back 170 times.

Ingots of aluminium are 9 metres (10 yards) long. That's enough to make over a million drinks cans.

These pieces are stretched and fixed together to make cans. They are then filled with cold, fizzy drinks and the tops, complete with ringpulls, are attached.

Again and again

Aluminium is ideal for packaging because it is light, strong, and easy to shape. It can be recycled again and again without affecting these properties. Aluminium cans are easily crushed and melted during recycling.

New versus recycled

Making cans from new aluminium uses a lot more **resources** than using recycled aluminium. It takes 5 tonnes of special crushed rock to make 1 tonne of new aluminium. Mining and processing the rock causes **pollution**. Making new aluminium ingots uses so much electricity that the factories where they are made need their own power plants. It takes twenty times more energy to make a new aluminium can than a recycled one.

Recycling one can like this saves enough energy to power a TV for three hours, run a lightbulb for twenty hours, power a small car for 1 kilometre (half a mile) or make nineteen more recycled cans.

{investigating energy sources}

Did you know we can **recycle** plant and animal waste to produce energy? **Biomass** is the word used for this sort of energy.

Lots of different types of waste are used as fuel for biomass. These include waste from timber yards, such as sawdust or wood chips, and waste left after **crops** have been processed, such as stubble or the pulp left after pressing oil out of olives. Livestock manure can also be used for biomass. As the manure **biodegrades** it releases methane gas, a kind of fuel that can be stored in tanks.

These fuels are burnt in ovens to release heat or in special **power stations** to produce electricity. Sometimes the waste fuel is topped up with wood from **plantations** of fast-growing trees such as willow. All the fuel used for biomass is **renewable**.

FACT!

- At the moment 2 litres (4 pints) of pig manure make a quarter of a litre (half a pint) of oil. Through its life, one pig could produce enough manure to make 80 litres (18 gallons) of oil.

- If half the US pig farms, some of which hold 10,000 pigs, made manure into oil, the USA would need to spend £3 billion less on buying oil each year.

From muck to money

Have you heard the expression 'where there's muck, there's brass'? It means there is money to be made from waste. An agricultural engineering professor in Illinois, USA, has discovered how to convert pig manure into oil! Professor Zhang uses special equipment to heat the manure under high pressure to form the oil. Just like **fossil fuel** oil, the manure oil can be made into diesel fuel or other products.

Pig farmers are very interested in Professor Zhang's idea. Manure is a major problem to them. If manure washes into rivers or lakes it causes **pollution**. Farmers need to carefully store manure in vast tanks. Now farmers pay to have the manure taken away. In future, they might be able to make money by selling their manure to oil makers. They would then make money from each pig they keep throughout its life rather than just when it is killed for its meat.

Professor Yuanhui Zhang in the USA is investigating ways of converting pig manure into oil.

{future choices}

Wasting **resources** and creating waste are worldwide problems. But as we have seen through this book, many of these problems can be tackled through **sustainable** living in the future.

Encouraging the Rs

More governments need to get behind the three Rs of sustainable living. They need to make it easier for people to reduce the resources they use, to reuse what they already have, and to **recycle**. But there is another R word that everyone needs to remember: responsibility.

People need to be more responsible for the waste they produce. For example, manufacturers of computers should be responsible for what they have made. This means using fewer resources and producing less waste to make them. It means designing computers that help save energy. But it also means making the computers easier to upgrade for reuse, to take apart for recycling or to dispose of without causing **pollution**.

Learning from others

Many people in **less-developed countries** have no choice but to live in a sustainable way. People who are poor cannot afford new stuff when it is broken so they fix it. They cannot afford to drive everywhere so they walk. People in **more-developed countries** should learn how to live using fewer resources. Several less-developed countries are becoming more industrialized and using up resources quicker. They need to develop carefully to be sustainable.

FACT!

It is estimated that 150 million computers are dumped in the USA alone. That's enough to fill a hole half a hectare (1 acre) wide and over 5 kilometres (3.5 miles) deep.

Using technology

We already have technology to help us live in a more sustainable way. However, it is not being used widely enough. For example, car manufacturers have already made experimental cars that do not run on **fossil fuels**. But this technology needs to be used widely now in order to slow down **global warming**. In the future manufacturers are likely to spend more time and money on developing cleaner cars.

Some technologies such as **solar cells** are not used more widely because they are expensive. If more people use them, however, they will be cheaper to buy. Governments can encourage sustainable technologies by educating people about their benefits. They can encourage manufacturers to make these technologies cheaper and easier to get hold of.

Technology that helps sustainable living is already with us. This woman is using solar power to do her cooking.

{further resources}

Books

Protecting Our Planet: Waste Recycling and Reuse, Steve Parker (Hodder Wayland, 2000)

50 Simple Things Kids Can Do to Save the Earth, The Earthworks Group (Warner Books)

Websites

You can explore the Internet to find out more about saving and recycling resources. Websites can change, so if the links below no longer work use a reliable search engine.

Ollie's Club and planet pals: Interactive fun, puzzles, and games about the 3 Rs, saving the planet and more at http://www.olliesworld.com/planet/index.htm and http://www.planetpals.com.

Several websites give details on where to send old computers to be repaired for reuse. For example, try www.computertakeback.com.

Many fair trade products are also organic. Learn more about fair trade by visiting its site:

www.fairtrade.org.uk

If you want to walk to school it is important you are safe on the roads. Check out www.roads.dtlr.gov.uk/roadsafety.highway/younghc.

Want to know more about organic food? Try http://www.soilassociation.org.

{glossary}

acid rain rainwater that has been polluted by chemicals in the air, making it acidic and damaging to wildlife

bacteria tiny living things found everywhere, in air, water, soils, and food. Some bacteria are good for us; others can cause disease.

biodegradable something that breaks down and rots away easily

biomass energy made from natural waste; for example, gas from animal dung can be used as fuel in power stations

cancer disease in which abnormal cells grow and spread. Cancer can be fatal.

cistern tank above the toilet that stores water

crops plants grown by farmers to sell

decomposers living things that can break down natural waste

deforestation when areas of forest are completely destroyed

environmental footprint how much land would be needed to provide all the resources a person needs and deal with the waste the person produces

evaporates when a liquid changes into a gas

fair trade fair trade companies pay people a fair wage for their skills and for the products they make

fertilizers chemical powders, sprays, or liquids used to improve soil and help plants grow

fossil fuels fuels such as oil, coal, and gas. They are formed from the remains of plants and animals that lived millions of years ago. They cannot be replaced.

geothermal energy obtained from the hot areas under the surface of the Earth

global warming rise in temperatures across the world, caused by the greenhouse effect

greenhouse effect blanket of gases in the air that are trapping heat

groundwater water found under the ground's surface, in cracks, or between bits of sand, soil, and gravel

incinerators large ovens for burning waste

insulate to stop heat escaping

irrigate to supply water for crops

landfill sites huge holes in the ground where waste is buried

leachate liquid from rotting waste that drains from landfill sites

less-developed countries Africa, most of Asia, Latin America and the Caribbean and Oceania (except for Australia and New Zealand)

logging cutting down trees for sale as timber

more-developed countries wealthier, more industrialized countries of the world, including Europe, Russia, USA, Canada, Australia, New Zealand, and Japan

non-renewable resources materials we use that will run out one day

organic farming that does not use chemicals such as pesticides

peat partially decayed plant matter in damp soil. Peat can be burnt when dried.

pesticides chemicals used to kill insects and other crop pests

photosynthesis process by which plants make food in their leaves, using water, carbon dioxide from the air, and energy from sunlight

plantation large area of land covered with a single crop that can be harvested again and again

pollution something that poisons or damages air, water, or land

power station factory that makes electricity

pulping using water to break down wood or paper in order to make new or recycled paper

recycling when waste is changed into something that can be used again

renewable something that can be replaced so it does not run out

resources materials and other things that people need and use

solar cell device that uses the Sun's energy for making electricity

sustainable something that keeps going and does not run out

temperate climate with warm, dry summers and cool, wet winters

tropical found in the tropics – countries around the Equator that have some of the hottest climates in the world

turbines blades that spin in moving air, steam, or water

water vapour when water is a gas in the air. Steam from a boiling kettle is a kind of water vapour.

{index}